MY
1000 HOURS OUTSIDE
JOURNEY

A COMPANION JOURNAL

This Journal Belongs to:

Starting Date:

Correspondence and comments?
Write to Ginny at:
Ginny@1000hoursoutside.com

This book is available at a
discount for retail, wholesale, bulk,
and promotional purchase. For more details,
email hello@1000hoursoutside.com.

Printed in the United States of America
First Printing: Fall 2021

Published by
SUNFLOWER HOUSE BOOKS

ISBN: 978-0-578-25443-2

It is worth your time to enter the wild.
In the wild, the brain is working at
full capacity, mapping out the next step
while rapidly assessing risk.
The body is constantly making adjustments,
adapting to the slick rock
or the unstable surface.
Nature time isn't just for leisure.
It is for building
robust brains and agile bodies.
It is for emotional development and
for bringing respite and delight.
It is for the whole child.
- Ginny Yurich

WELCOME TO YOUR 1000 HOURS OUTSIDE JOURNEY

Childhood is a time for developing the whole child. When children are free to play and explore outside from birth through graduation, those opportunties help them develop in every facet of their being.

Time outside helps children cognitively through a myriad of ways. Beyond physically getting them ready for seat work through large motor and fine motor enhancement, the complex movements that children engage in outdoors enhance brain function. Active free play is essential to learning.

Beyond academic benefits, outdoor play facilitates growth in three key areas of development: social, physical and emotional. The benefits are truly astounding and the research is lengthy and far-reaching.

By being intentional about nature play, you will give your children lifelong advantages. As simple as it sounds, a year filled with hundreds of hours in the open air will enhance childhood beyond what you could ever imagine.

The good news here is that it doesn't matter what climate you live in or what nature experiences are around you. Wherever you are, nature will provide a dazzling array of opportunities to engage the senses and further development.

In "How to Raise a Wild Child", Dr. Scott D. Sampson quotes a study that states the average American child only gets 4-7 minutes of active free play outdoors a day. Pediatric occupational therapists, such as Angela Hanscom and Carla Hannaford, are saying that lack of time for outside movement is contributing to a whole host of developmental delays.

Here's the good news - by making one simple change of prioritizing nature time, you will revolutionize childhood, contribute to every facet of child development, build memories, experience joy, and uniquely build a foundation for your family or classroom. You'll also gain all sorts of benefits for yourself. Nature enhances our lives at every age.

You've got your pencils. You've got your crayons. You've got your paper. You've got your textbooks. You've got your backpack. You've got all your learning supplies. Don't forget add the wonder. Join us on this simple, yet extremely impactful journey of deliberately adding outside time to your lives.

HOW TO USE THIS COMPANION JOURNAL

I'm not certain of much, but I am absolutely certain that a year filled with simple nature experiences will be a grand year indeed.

Use your companion journal to remember, to celebrate, and to model striving for balance in a tech-saturated world.

Your companion journal has four components. As you move through the weeks, your outside logs may not always align perfectly with your milestone tracker sheets - this is okay! Move at your own pace and enjoy the journey.

Each season you'll find a bucket list. Circle which season you are in and fill in the top seasonal activities that you don't want to miss.

Each week you'll find a weekly log that includes places to track your hours, track the weather, jot down a short journal entry, and color in a sun if you got outside before noon. Exposure to morning sunshine helps reset your body rhythms.

You will notice that beyond the initial 1000 Hours Outside mandala tracker, your journal also includes milestone trackers for each 100 hours spent outside. Many families like to celebrate these smaller milestones.

This is not a competition. It is a movement. It is a shift back to the baseline needs of children. By joining this journey, and filling out your companion journal, you are modeling to your family the importance of balance between real-world and virtual.

BUT WHAT IF I FAIL?

Then you win.

You win because the average American child spends around 25 - 40 hours a year in free play outside but 1200 hours a year on screens and you, my friend are helping to restore a balance to childhood that is desperately needed.

You win because with every moment, with every rock thrown and every snowball formed, you are allowing your child to flourish.

You win because the memories will pile up.
It doesn't need to be expensive to experience some of life's most thrilling moments.

You win because I believe you will be a better parent. Mother Nature takes the edge off. It's the way it was meant to be. Kids come at life with a relentless energy as they pursue this grand task of becoming themselves and nature welcomes and helps absorb their boundless spirits.

Change your life and transform childhood with the simple goal of prioritizing nature. You will all be better for it- whether you hit 1,000 hours or more or less.

"Nature is not a place to visit. It is *home.*"
— Gary Snyder

JAN .... FEB .... MAR .... APR .... MAY .... JUN ....

JUL .... AUG .... SEP .... OCT .... NOV .... DEC ....

SEASONAL BUCKET LIST

WINTER/SPRING/SUMMER/FALL
(circle one)

○

○

○

○

○

○

○

○

○

○

○

An interesting sight

A favorite activity

Something memorable

New thing learned

OUTSIDE L⊚G

	TIME OUTSIDE	JOURNAL ENTRY	WEATHER	SUNLIGHT BEFORE NOON
Sunday				☀
Monday	3/6/23 12pm – 4pm	OUTDOOR PLAY / SCHOOLWORK	SUNNY	☀
Tuesday				☀
Wednesday				☀
Thursday				☀
Friday				☀
Saturday				☀

An interesting sight

A favorite activity

Something memorable

New thing learned

OUTSIDE LOG

WEEK OF _____

	TIME OUTSIDE	JOURNAL ENTRY	WEATHER	SUNLIGHT BEFORE NOON
Sunday				
Monday				
Tuesday				
Wednesday				
Thursday				
Friday				
Saturday				

An interesting sight

A favorite activity

Something memorable

New thing learned

OUTSIDE L⊙G

WEEK OF _____

	TIME OUTSIDE	JOURNAL ENTRY	WEATHER	SUNLIGHT BEFORE NOON
Sunday				
Monday				
Tuesday				
Wednesday				
Thursday				
Friday				
Saturday				

An interesting sight

A favorite activity

Something
memorable

New thing
learned

The adults plod along,
the children twirl, leap, skip,
run now to this side and now to that,
look for things to step or jump over
or walk along or around,
climb on anything that can be climbed.
I never want to be where I cannot see it.
All that energy and foolishness,
all that curiosity, questions, talk,
all those fierce passions, inconsolable sorrows,
immoderate joys... To me they are a
national asset, a treasure beyond price...

- John Holt

200

25 · · 25

· 100 ·

· 50 ·

· 75 ·

FAVORITE OUTDOOR MEMORY:

OUTSIDE L☉G

	TIME OUTSIDE	JOURNAL ENTRY	WEATHER	SUNLIGHT BEFORE NOON
Sunday				
Monday				
Tuesday				
Wednesday				
Thursday				
Friday				
Saturday				

An interesting sight

A favorite activity

Something memorable

New thing learned

OUTSIDE LOG

WEEK OF _____

	TIME OUTSIDE	JOURNAL ENTRY	WEATHER	SUNLIGHT BEFORE NOON
Sunday				
Monday				
Tuesday				
Wednesday				
Thursday				
Friday				
Saturday				

An interesting sight

A favorite activity

Something memorable

New thing learned

OUTSIDE LOG

WEEK OF _____

	TIME OUTSIDE	JOURNAL ENTRY	WEATHER	SUNLIGHT BEFORE NOON
Sunday				
Monday				
Tuesday				
Wednesday				
Thursday				
Friday				
Saturday				

An interesting sight

A favorite activity

Something
memorable

New thing
learned

OUTSIDE L☉G

	TIME OUTSIDE	JOURNAL ENTRY	WEATHER	SUNLIGHT BEFORE NOON
Sunday				☀
Monday				☀
Tuesday				☀
Wednesday				☀
Thursday				☀
Friday				☀
Saturday				☀

An interesting sight

A favorite activity

Something
memorable

New thing
learned

Self-education through play and exploration
requires enormous amounts
of unscheduled time -
time to do whatever one wants to do,
without pressure, judgment,
or intrusion from authority figures.
That time is needed to make friends,
play with ideas and materials,
experience and overcome boredom,
learn from one's own mistakes,
and develop passions.

- Peter Gray

300

25

50

75

100

FAVORITE OUTDOOR MEMORY:

OUTSIDE LOG

WEEK OF _____

	TIME OUTSIDE	JOURNAL ENTRY	WEATHER	SUNLIGHT BEFORE NOON
Sunday				
Monday				
Tuesday				
Wednesday				
Thursday				
Friday				
Saturday				

An interesting sight

A favorite activity

Something memorable

New thing learned

OUTSIDE L⊙G

	TIME OUTSIDE	JOURNAL ENTRY	WEATHER	SUNLIGHT BEFORE NOON
Sunday				☀
Monday				☀
Tuesday				☀
Wednesday				☀
Thursday				☀
Friday				☀
Saturday				☀

An interesting sight

A favorite activity

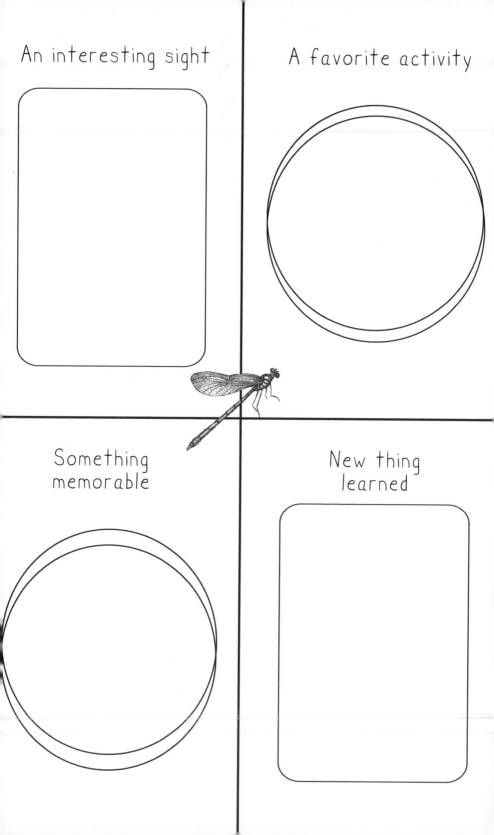

Something
memorable

New thing
learned

OUTSIDE LOG

WEEK OF _____

	TIME OUTSIDE	JOURNAL ENTRY	WEATHER	SUNLIGHT BEFORE NOON
Sunday				
Monday				
Tuesday				
Wednesday				
Thursday				
Friday				
Saturday				

An interesting sight

A favorite activity

Something
memorable

New thing
learned

OUTSIDE LOG

WEEK OF _____

	TIME OUTSIDE	JOURNAL ENTRY	WEATHER	SUNLIGHT BEFORE NOON
Sunday				☀
Monday				☀
Tuesday				☀
Wednesday				☀
Thursday				☀
Friday				☀
Saturday				☀

An interesting sight

A favorite activity

Something
memorable

New thing
learned

SEASONAL BUCKET LIST

WINTER/SPRING/SUMMER/FALL
(circle one)

- ◯
- ◯
- ◯
- ◯
- ◯
- ◯
- ◯
- ◯
- ◯
- ◯
- ◯

400

25

50

75

100

FAVORITE OUTDOOR MEMORY:

OUTSIDE L☉G

WEEK OF _____

	TIME OUTSIDE	JOURNAL ENTRY	WEATHER	SUNLIGHT BEFORE NOON
Sunday				
Monday				
Tuesday				
Wednesday				
Thursday				
Friday				
Saturday				

An interesting sight

A favorite activity

Something
memorable

New thing
learned

OUTSIDE LOG

WEEK OF _____

	TIME OUTSIDE	JOURNAL ENTRY	WEATHER	SUNLIGHT BEFORE NOON
Sunday				
Monday				
Tuesday				
Wednesday				
Thursday				
Friday				
Saturday				

An interesting sight

A favorite activity

Something memorable

New thing learned

OUTSIDE L☉G

	TIME OUTSIDE	JOURNAL ENTRY	WEATHER	SUNLIGHT BEFORE NOON
Sunday				☀
Monday				☀
Tuesday				☀
Wednesday				☀
Thursday				☀
Friday				☀
Saturday				☀

An interesting sight

A favorite activity

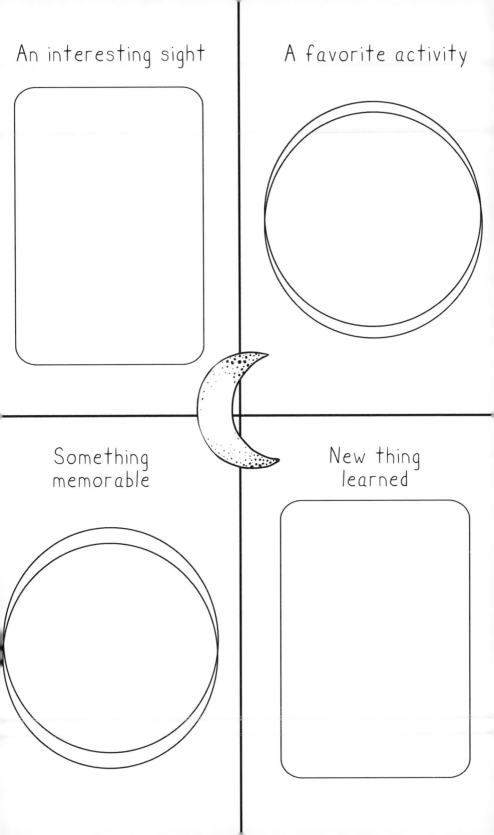

Something
memorable

New thing
learned

OUTSIDE L⊙G

WEEK OF _____

	TIME OUTSIDE	JOURNAL ENTRY	WEATHER	SUNLIGHT BEFORE NOON
Sunday				
Monday				
Tuesday				
Wednesday				
Thursday				
Friday				
Saturday				

An interesting sight

A favorite activity

Something
memorable

New thing
learned

OUTSIDE LOG

WEEK OF _____

	TIME OUTSIDE	JOURNAL ENTRY	WEATHER	SUNLIGHT BEFORE NOON
Sunday				
Monday				
Tuesday				
Wednesday				
Thursday				
Friday				
Saturday				

An interesting sight

A favorite activity

Something
memorable

New thing
learned

OUTSIDE L🪵G

	TIME OUTSIDE	JOURNAL ENTRY	WEATHER	SUNLIGHT BEFORE NOON
Sunday				
Monday				
Tuesday				
Wednesday				
Thursday				
Friday				
Saturday				

An interesting sight

A favorite activity

Something
memorable

New thing
learned

OUTSIDE LOG

WEEK OF _____

	TIME OUTSIDE	JOURNAL ENTRY	WEATHER	SUNLIGHT BEFORE NOON
Sunday				
Monday				
Tuesday				
Wednesday				
Thursday				
Friday				
Saturday				

An interesting sight

A favorite activity

Something
memorable

New thing
learned

Learn to like what doesn't cost much.
Learn to like reading, conversation, music.
Learn to like plain food,
plain service, plain cooking.
Learn to like fields, trees, brooks,
hiking, rowing, climbing hills.
Learn to like people, even though
some of them may be different.
Different from you.
Learn to like work and enjoy
the satisfaction of doing your job
as well as it can be done.
Learn to like gardening,
puttering around the house, and fixing things.
Learn to like the sunrise and the sunset,
the beating of rain on the roof and windows,
and the gentle fall of snow on a winter day.
Learn to keep your wants simple,
and refuse to be controlled by the
likes and dislikes of others.

- Lowell C. Bennion

500

FAVORITE OUTDOOR MEMORY:

OUTSIDE L☉G

WEEK OF _____

	TIME OUTSIDE	JOURNAL ENTRY	WEATHER	SUNLIGHT BEFORE NOON
Sunday				☀
Monday				☀
Tuesday				☀
Wednesday				☀
Thursday				☀
Friday				☀
Saturday				☀

An interesting sight

A favorite activity

Something
memorable

New thing
learned

OUTSIDE L☉G

	TIME OUTSIDE	JOURNAL ENTRY	WEATHER	SUNLIGHT BEFORE NOON
Sunday				
Monday				
Tuesday				
Wednesday				
Thursday				
Friday				
Saturday				

An interesting sight

A favorite activity

Something
memorable

New thing
learned

OUTSIDE LOG

WEEK OF _____

	TIME OUTSIDE	JOURNAL ENTRY	WEATHER	SUNLIGHT BEFORE NOON
Sunday				
Monday				
Tuesday				
Wednesday				
Thursday				
Friday				
Saturday				

An interesting sight

A favorite activity

Something memorable

New thing learned

OUTSIDE L⊚G

	TIME OUTSIDE	JOURNAL ENTRY	WEATHER	SUNLIGHT BEFORE NOON
Sunday				
Monday				
Tuesday				
Wednesday				
Thursday				
Friday				
Saturday				

An interesting sight

A favorite activity

Something
memorable

New thing
learned

OUTSIDE L🪵G

	TIME OUTSIDE	JOURNAL ENTRY	WEATHER	SUNLIGHT BEFORE NOON
Sunday				☀
Monday				☀
Tuesday				☀
Wednesday				☀
Thursday				☀
Friday				☀
Saturday				☀

An interesting sight

A favorite activity

Something
memorable

New thing
learned

OUTSIDE LOG

WEEK OF _____

	TIME OUTSIDE	JOURNAL ENTRY	WEATHER	SUNLIGHT BEFORE NOON
Sunday				
Monday				
Tuesday				
Wednesday				
Thursday				
Friday				
Saturday				

An interesting sight

A favorite activity

Something
memorable

New thing
learned

SEASONAL BUCKET LIST

WINTER/SPRING/SUMMER/FALL
(circle one)

- ◯
- ◯
- ◯
- ◯
- ◯
- ◯
- ◯
- ◯
- ◯
- ◯
- ◯

600

FAVORITE OUTDOOR MEMORY:

OUTSIDE L☉G

SUNLIGHT
BEFORE
NOON

	TIME OUTSIDE	JOURNAL ENTRY	WEATHER	
Sunday				
Monday				
Tuesday				
Wednesday				
Thursday				
Friday				
Saturday				

An interesting sight

A favorite activity

Something
memorable

New thing
learned

OUTSIDE L☉G

	TIME OUTSIDE	JOURNAL ENTRY	WEATHER	SUNLIGHT BEFORE NOON
Sunday				☼
Monday				☼
Tuesday				☼
Wednesday				☼
Thursday				☼
Friday				☼
Saturday				☼

An interesting sight

A favorite activity

Something
memorable

New thing
learned

OUTSIDE LOG

WEEK OF _____

	TIME OUTSIDE	JOURNAL ENTRY	WEATHER	SUNLIGHT BEFORE NOON
Sunday				
Monday				
Tuesday				
Wednesday				
Thursday				
Friday				
Saturday				

An interesting sight

A favorite activity

Something
memorable

New thing
learned

OUTSIDE L⊙G

	TIME OUTSIDE	JOURNAL ENTRY	WEATHER	SUNLIGHT BEFORE NOON
Sunday				
Monday				
Tuesday				
Wednesday				
Thursday				
Friday				
Saturday				

An interesting sight

A favorite activity

Something
memorable

New thing
learned

OUTSIDE LOG

WEEK OF _____

	TIME OUTSIDE	JOURNAL ENTRY	WEATHER	SUNLIGHT BEFORE NOON
Sunday				
Monday				
Tuesday				
Wednesday				
Thursday				
Friday				
Saturday				

An interesting sight

A favorite activity

Something
memorable

New thing
learned

OUTSIDE LOG

	TIME OUTSIDE	JOURNAL ENTRY	WEATHER	SUNLIGHT BEFORE NOON
Sunday				
Monday				
Tuesday				
Wednesday				
Thursday				
Friday				
Saturday				

An interesting sight

A favorite activity

Something
memorable

New thing
learned

OUTSIDE LOG

	TIME OUTSIDE	JOURNAL ENTRY	WEATHER	SUNLIGHT BEFORE NOON
Sunday				
Monday				
Tuesday				
Wednesday				
Thursday				
Friday				
Saturday				

An interesting sight

A favorite activity

Something
memorable

New thing
learned

What the child
finds worthy,
is worthy.

- Ginny Yurich

700

25

50

75

100

FAVORITE OUTDOOR MEMORY:

OUTSIDE L🪵G

	TIME OUTSIDE	JOURNAL ENTRY	WEATHER	SUNLIGHT BEFORE NOON
Sunday				
Monday				
Tuesday				
Wednesday				
Thursday				
Friday				
Saturday				

An interesting sight

A favorite activity

Something
memorable

New thing
learned

OUTSIDE LOG

	TIME OUTSIDE	JOURNAL ENTRY	WEATHER	SUNLIGHT BEFORE NOON
Sunday				☀
Monday				☀
Tuesday				☀
Wednesday				☀
Thursday				☀
Friday				☀
Saturday				☀

An interesting sight

A favorite activity

Something
memorable

New thing
learned

OUTSIDE L⊙G

	TIME OUTSIDE	JOURNAL ENTRY	WEATHER	SUNLIGHT BEFORE NOON
Sunday				☀
Monday				☀
Tuesday				☀
Wednesday				☀
Thursday				☀
Friday				☀
Saturday				☀

An interesting sight

A favorite activity

Something
memorable

New thing
learned

OUTSIDE L☉G

	TIME OUTSIDE	JOURNAL ENTRY	WEATHER	SUNLIGHT BEFORE NOON
Sunday				☀
Monday				☀
Tuesday				☀
Wednesday				☀
Thursday				☀
Friday				☀
Saturday				☀

An interesting sight

A favorite activity

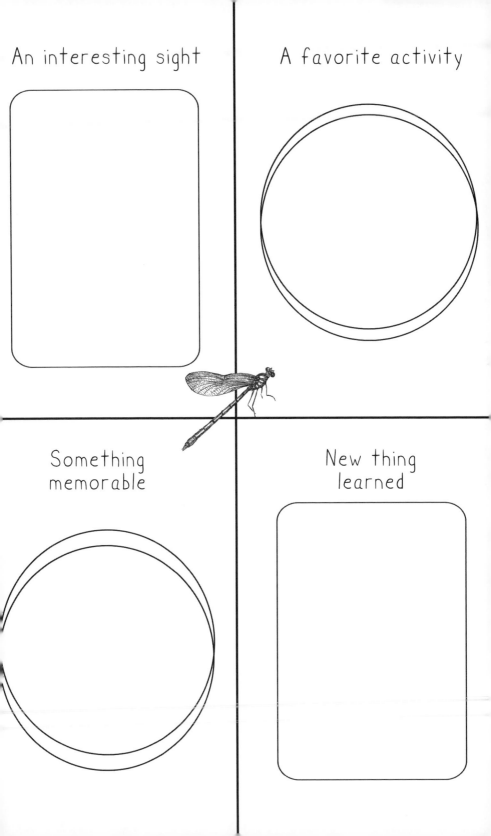

Something
memorable

New thing
learned

OUTSIDE LOG

WEEK OF _____

	TIME OUTSIDE	JOURNAL ENTRY	WEATHER	SUNLIGHT BEFORE NOON
Sunday				
Monday				
Tuesday				
Wednesday				
Thursday				
Friday				
Saturday				

An interesting sight

A favorite activity

Something memorable

New thing learned

OUTSIDE LOG

WEEK OF _____

	TIME OUTSIDE	JOURNAL ENTRY	WEATHER	SUNLIGHT BEFORE NOON
Sunday				
Monday				
Tuesday				
Wednesday				
Thursday				
Friday				
Saturday				

An interesting sight

A favorite activity

Something
memorable

New thing
learned

SEASONAL BUCKET LIST

WINTER/SPRING/SUMMER/FALL
(circle one)

- ◯
- ◯
- ◯
- ◯
- ◯
- ◯
- ◯
- ◯
- ◯
- ◯
- ◯

800

25

100

50

75

FAVORITE OUTDOOR MEMORY:

OUTSIDE L⊙G

	TIME OUTSIDE	JOURNAL ENTRY	WEATHER	SUNLIGHT BEFORE NOON
Sunday				
Monday				
Tuesday				
Wednesday				
Thursday				
Friday				
Saturday				

An interesting sight

A favorite activity

Something memorable

New thing learned

OUTSIDE LOG

WEEK OF _____

	TIME OUTSIDE	JOURNAL ENTRY	WEATHER	SUNLIGHT BEFORE NOON
Sunday				
Monday				
Tuesday				
Wednesday				
Thursday				
Friday				
Saturday				

An interesting sight

A favorite activity

Something
memorable

New thing
learned

OUTSIDE L☉G

	TIME OUTSIDE	JOURNAL ENTRY	WEATHER	SUNLIGHT BEFORE NOON
Sunday				☀
Monday				☀
Tuesday				☀
Wednesday				☀
Thursday				☀
Friday				☀
Saturday				☀

An interesting sight

A favorite activity

Something
memorable

New thing
learned

OUTSIDE L☉G

WEEK OF _____

	TIME OUTSIDE	JOURNAL ENTRY	WEATHER	SUNLIGHT BEFORE NOON
Sunday				☀
Monday				☀
Tuesday				☀
Wednesday				☀
Thursday				☀
Friday				☀
Saturday				☀

An interesting sight

A favorite activity

Something
memorable

New thing
learned

OUTSIDE LOG

SUNLIGHT
BEFORE
NOON

	TIME OUTSIDE	JOURNAL ENTRY	WEATHER	
Sunday				
Monday				
Tuesday				
Wednesday				
Thursday				
Friday				
Saturday				

An interesting sight

A favorite activity

Something
memorable

New thing
learned

Extraordinary moments lie in the puddle stomps,
the flower petals adorning the mud pie,
the spray of the sea,
and the dance of the bonfire light.

They hang from the tree limbs,
march in tiny specks across the sidewalks,
and fall from the sky as frozen crystals.
They are visible in the bright dawn of morning,
in the evening sky that's been filled with cotton candy,
and overhead on a clear, dark night.

The extraordinary moments are indeed all around us.

A year that includes 1000 hours of the sights,
sounds, and smells of nature will fill your life
to the brim and provide immense joys.

Slow down and yet gain more
through nature play.

- Ginny Yurich

900

FAVORITE OUTDOOR MEMORY:

OUTSIDE L☉G

	TIME OUTSIDE	JOURNAL ENTRY	WEATHER	SUNLIGHT BEFORE NOON
Sunday				☀
Monday				☀
Tuesday				☀
Wednesday				☀
Thursday				☀
Friday				☀
Saturday				☀

An interesting sight

A favorite activity

Something memorable

New thing learned

OUTSIDE L☉G

WEEK OF _____

	TIME OUTSIDE	JOURNAL ENTRY	WEATHER	SUNLIGHT BEFORE NOON
Sunday				
Monday				
Tuesday				
Wednesday				
Thursday				
Friday				
Saturday				

An interesting sight

A favorite activity

Something memorable

New thing learned

OUTSIDE L🪵G

	TIME OUTSIDE	JOURNAL ENTRY	WEATHER	SUNLIGHT BEFORE NOON
Sunday				
Monday				
Tuesday				
Wednesday				
Thursday				
Friday				
Saturday				

An interesting sight

A favorite activity

Something
memorable

New thing
learned

OUTSIDE L⊙G

	TIME OUTSIDE	JOURNAL ENTRY	WEATHER	SUNLIGHT BEFORE NOON
Sunday				
Monday				
Tuesday				
Wednesday				
Thursday				
Friday				
Saturday				

An interesting sight

A favorite activity

Something memorable

New thing learned

Living is learning and
when kids are living fully
and energetically and happily
they are learning a lot,
even if we don't always
know what it is

- John Holt

1000

FAVORITE OUTDOOR MEMORY:

OUTSIDE L⊙G

	TIME OUTSIDE	JOURNAL ENTRY	WEATHER	SUNLIGHT BEFORE NOON
Sunday				
Monday				
Tuesday				
Wednesday				
Thursday				
Friday				
Saturday				

An interesting sight

A favorite activity

Something
memorable

New thing
learned

OUTSIDE L⊙G

	TIME OUTSIDE	JOURNAL ENTRY	WEATHER	SUNLIGHT BEFORE NOON
Sunday				
Monday				
Tuesday				
Wednesday				
Thursday				
Friday				
Saturday				

An interesting sight

A favorite activity

Something
memorable

New thing
learned

OUTSIDE L🪵G

WEEK OF _____

	TIME OUTSIDE	JOURNAL ENTRY	WEATHER	SUNLIGHT BEFORE NOON
Sunday				☀
Monday				☀
Tuesday				☀
Wednesday				☀
Thursday				☀
Friday				☀
Saturday				☀

An interesting sight

A favorite activity

Something
memorable

New thing
learned

OUTSIDE L☉G

	TIME OUTSIDE	JOURNAL ENTRY	WEATHER	SUNLIGHT BEFORE NOON
Sunday				☀
Monday				☀
Tuesday				☀
Wednesday				☀
Thursday				☀
Friday				☀
Saturday				☀

An interesting sight

A favorite activity

Something memorable

New thing learned

MAYBE

Maybe you'll stay at the playground just a little bit longer
Maybe you'll build a snow fort or a stick fort or a fort that's hidden
within the branches of a tree
Maybe you'll go on a lantern hike
Maybe you'll try camping for the very first time
Maybe you'll star gaze
Maybe you'll discover the wildlife that's all around you
Maybe you'll explore a brand new path
Maybe you'll get up early for a sunrise
Maybe you'll splash in ocean waves
Maybe you'll influence a friend
Maybe you'll grow something in the garden that you've never grown
before
Maybe you'll learn how to forage
Maybe you'll picnic along a riverbank
Maybe you'll read a riveting book in a hammock
Maybe you'll set aside those always present, always pressing tasks for
some breeze through your hair
Maybe you'll take an extra loop around the neighborhood
Maybe you'll become a sidewalk chalk artist
Maybe you'll start a nature group
Maybe you'll spend some time with your toes in the grass
Maybe you'll bring back the simple joys of jump rope, hopscotch and
four square
Maybe you'll stay out just a little bit longer and play just a little bit
more, rooted in the knowledge that time for nature play is one of the
best gifts we can give our kids
Maybe you'll hit 1000 hours, maybe more, maybe less
Wherever your nature journey takes you, you don't have to wonder
about the outcome. Nature play always supplies troves of smiles,
memories, and foundational life experiences that contribute immensely
to whole-child development.

Join us. It's as simple as prioritizing 1000 little circles that represent
more life lived than you could ever imagine.

FOR MORE INFORMATION:

www.1000hoursoutside.com
@1000hoursoutside
#1000hoursoutside

1000 HOURS
OUTSIDE™